Ordering Numbers and Rounding

1. Put these numbers in order. Start with the **largest**.

| 121 | 452 | 683 | 119 | 813 | 640 |

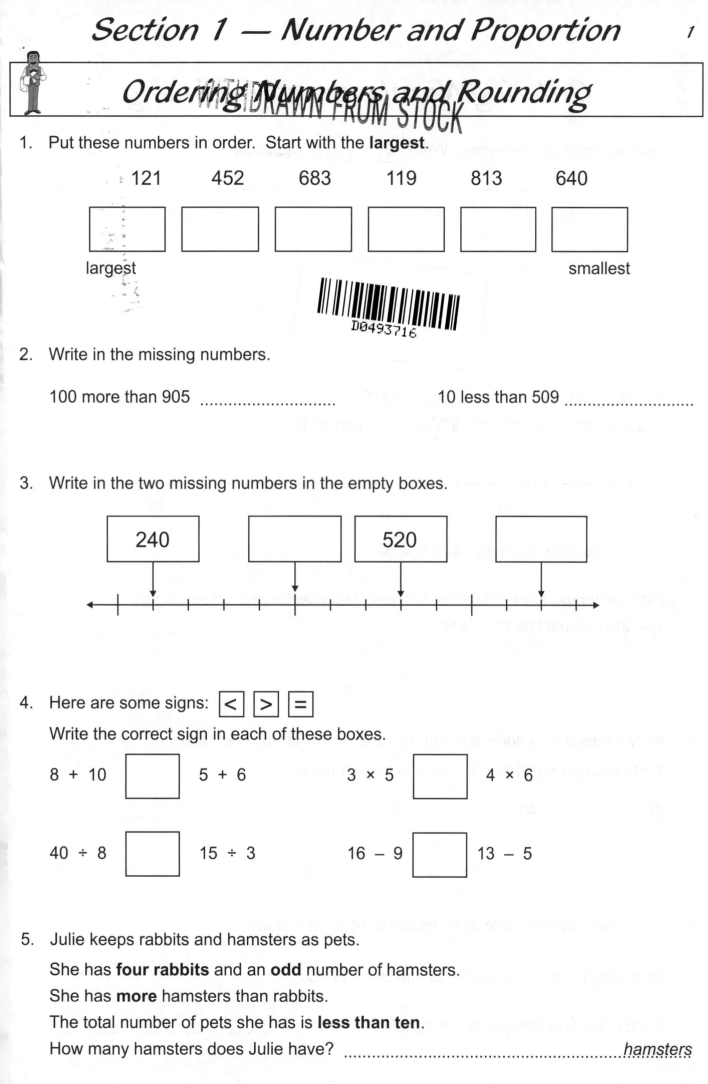

largest   smallest

2. Write in the missing numbers.

    100 more than 905 ....   10 less than 509 ....

3. Write in the two missing numbers in the empty boxes.

    | 240 | | 520 | |

4. Here are some signs: < > =

    Write the correct sign in each of these boxes.

    8 + 10 ☐ 5 + 6   3 × 5 ☐ 4 × 6

    40 ÷ 8 ☐ 15 ÷ 3   16 − 9 ☐ 13 − 5

5. Julie keeps rabbits and hamsters as pets.

    She has **four rabbits** and an **odd** number of hamsters.

    She has **more** hamsters than rabbits.

    The total number of pets she has is **less than ten**.

    How many hamsters does Julie have? .... *hamsters*

Ordering Numbers and Rounding

6. Look at these temperatures. Write $<$ or $>$ in each box.

    17 °C ☐ 19 °C   8 °C ☐ –8 °C

    –4 °C ☐ –12 °C   0 °C ☐ –5 °C

7. The temperature in Copenhagen is **–9 °C**.

    Draw an arrow pointing to **–9 °C** on this number line.

    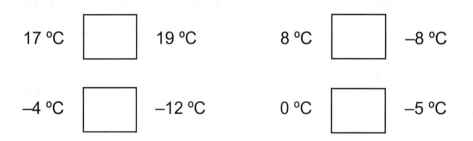

    The temperature in Manchester is **3 °C**.

    Find the temperature difference between Manchester and Copenhagen.
    Use the number line to help you. ....°C

8. Kelly writes a sequence of numbers. She **subtracts 35** each time.

    Write down the next two numbers in this sequence.

    80   45   10   ....

9. The temperature outside Jeff's house is **14 °C** at midday.

    By midnight, the temperature has fallen by **27 °C**.

    What is the temperature at midnight? ....°C

Ordering Numbers and Rounding

10. Which of these numbers is closest to 300? Circle the correct number.

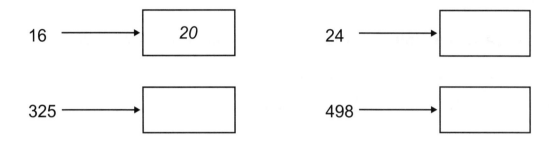

| 280 | 400 | 349 | 325 | 250 |

11. Round these numbers to the nearest 10. One has been done for you.

16 ⟶ 20   24 ⟶

325 ⟶   498 ⟶

12. Round these numbers to the nearest 100. Write your answers in the boxes.

64 ⟶   837 ⟶

952 ⟶   149 ⟶

13. What is **12 345** rounded to the nearest 1000? ....

14. Round each of these decimals to the nearest whole number.

1.8   3.49

15. Round each of these decimals to the nearest tenth.

9.15   6.549

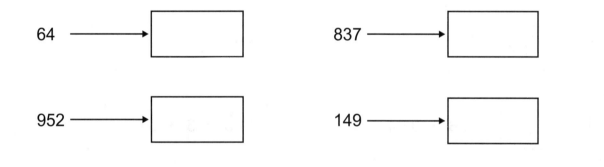

A Number Adder knows how to use a number line.
Do you? Tick the box to say how you feel.

Decimals

1. Here is a number line. Write the two missing numbers in the boxes.

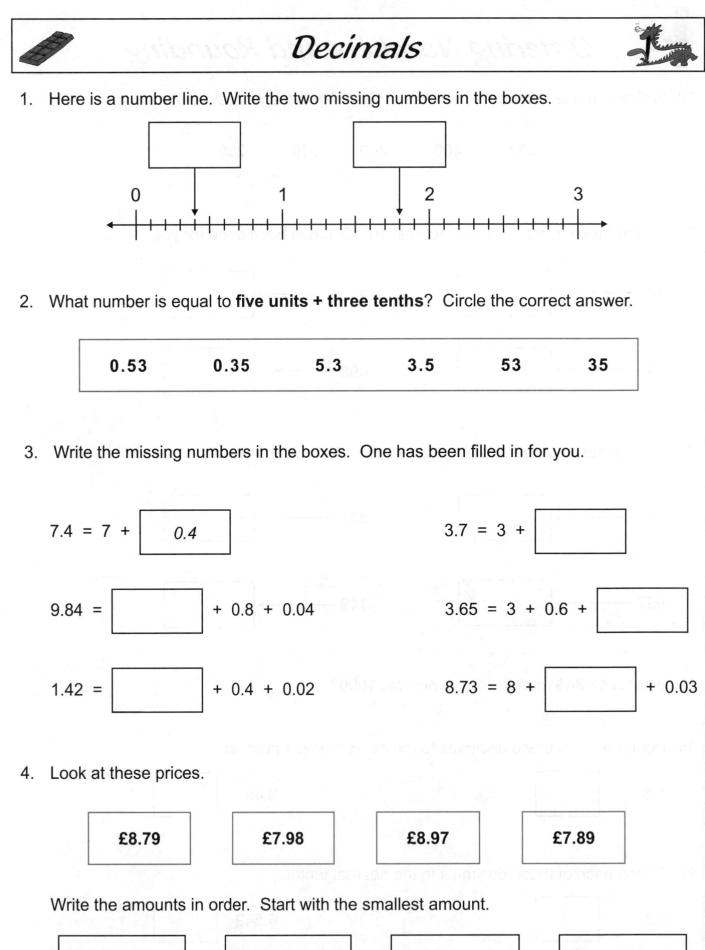

2. What number is equal to **five units + three tenths**? Circle the correct answer.

| 0.53 | 0.35 | 5.3 | 3.5 | 53 | 35 |

3. Write the missing numbers in the boxes. One has been filled in for you.

7.4 = 7 + $\boxed{0.4}$

3.7 = 3 + $\boxed{}$

9.84 = $\boxed{}$ + 0.8 + 0.04

3.65 = 3 + 0.6 + $\boxed{}$

1.42 = $\boxed{}$ + 0.4 + 0.02

8.73 = 8 + $\boxed{}$ + 0.03

4. Look at these prices.

| £8.79 | £7.98 | £8.97 | £7.89 |

Write the amounts in order. Start with the smallest amount.

| £ | £ | £ | £ |

smallest   largest

Decimals

5. Look at this number line. Write the numbers shown by the arrows.

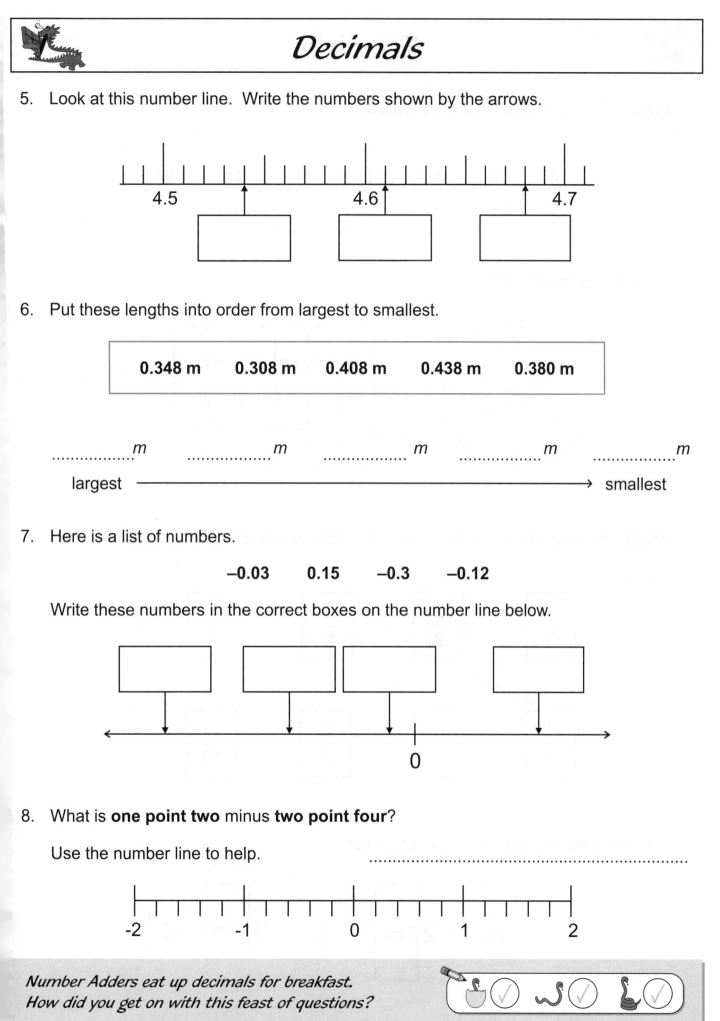

4.5   4.6   4.7

6. Put these lengths into order from largest to smallest.

0.348 m   0.308 m   0.408 m   0.438 m   0.380 m

.... m   .... m   .... m   .... m   .... m

largest ──→ smallest

7. Here is a list of numbers.

−0.03   0.15   −0.3   −0.12

Write these numbers in the correct boxes on the number line below.

0

8. What is **one point two** minus **two point four**?

Use the number line to help.   ....

-2   -1   0   1   2

Fractions

1. What is $\frac{1}{4}$ of 28? Circle the correct answer.

4	7	8	10	14	18	24

2. Shade $\frac{2}{3}$ of each shape.

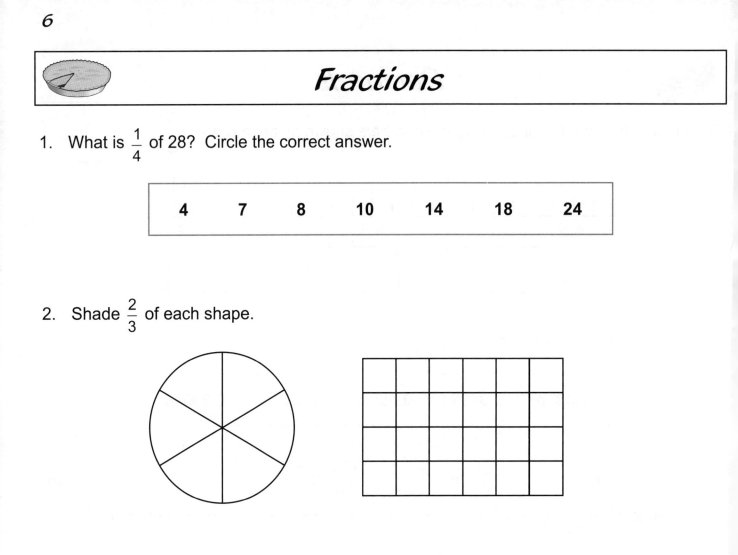

3. Match the boxes that have the same value. One has been done for you.

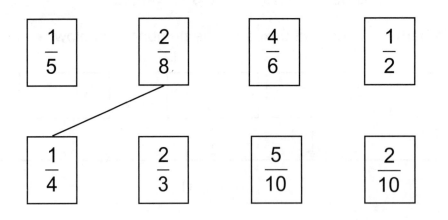

$$\frac{1}{5} \qquad \frac{2}{8} \qquad \frac{4}{6} \qquad \frac{1}{2}$$

$$\frac{1}{4} \qquad \frac{2}{3} \qquad \frac{5}{10} \qquad \frac{2}{10}$$

4. Fill in the missing fractions in this sequence.

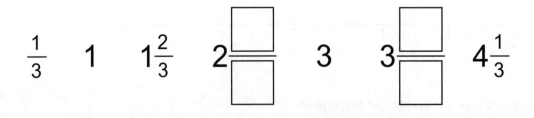

$$\frac{1}{3} \qquad 1 \qquad 1\frac{2}{3} \qquad 2\frac{\square}{\square} \qquad 3 \qquad 3\frac{\square}{\square} \qquad 4\frac{1}{3}$$

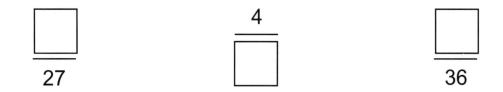

Fractions

5. Complete these fractions to make each equivalent to $\frac{2}{9}$.

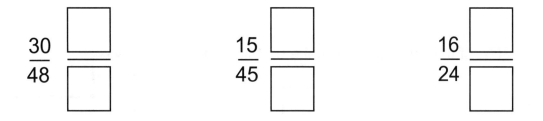

$$\frac{\square}{27} \qquad \frac{4}{\square} \qquad \frac{\square}{36}$$

6. Write these fractions in their simplest form.

$$\frac{30}{48} \, \frac{\square}{\square} \qquad \frac{15}{45} \, \frac{\square}{\square} \qquad \frac{16}{24} \, \frac{\square}{\square}$$

7. Write these fractions in order of size.

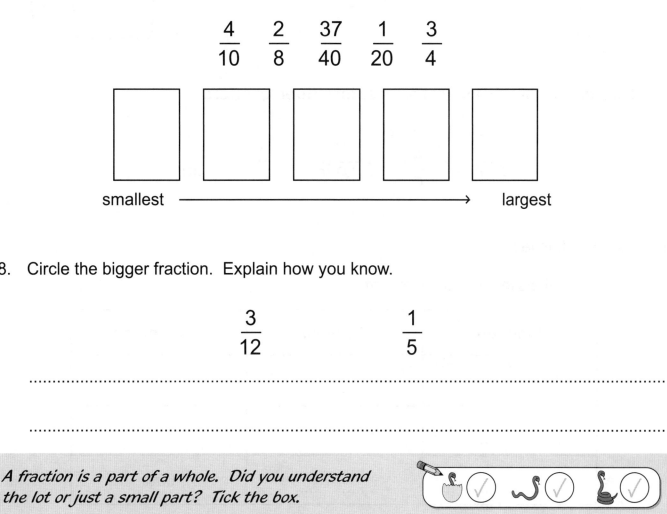

$$\frac{4}{10} \qquad \frac{2}{8} \qquad \frac{37}{40} \qquad \frac{1}{20} \qquad \frac{3}{4}$$

smallest ⟶ largest

8. Circle the bigger fraction. Explain how you know.

$$\frac{3}{12} \qquad\qquad \frac{1}{5}$$

....

....

A fraction is a part of a whole. Did you understand
the lot or just a small part? Tick the box.

Percentages

1. Write these fractions as percentages and decimals. One has been done for you.

$\dfrac{45}{100}$ percentage ....45%..........

   decimal ....0.45.........

$\dfrac{13}{100}$ percentage ....%

   decimal ....

$\dfrac{7}{10}$ percentage ....%

   decimal ....

$\dfrac{9}{10}$ percentage ....%

   decimal ....

2. Shade in **30%** of the squares that make up this shape:

   What fraction have you shaded? $\dfrac{\boxed{}}{\boxed{}}$

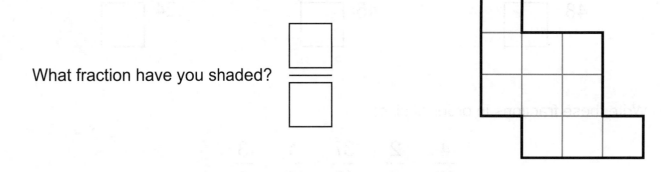

3. Circle the amounts below that are less than **three quarters**.

   28% $\dfrac{4}{5}$ 76% $\dfrac{2}{3}$ 35%

4. Complete this table.

   Give all fractions in their simplest form.

Fraction	Decimal	Percentage
$\dfrac{1}{4}$	....	....
....	0.5	....
....	....	60%

Percentages

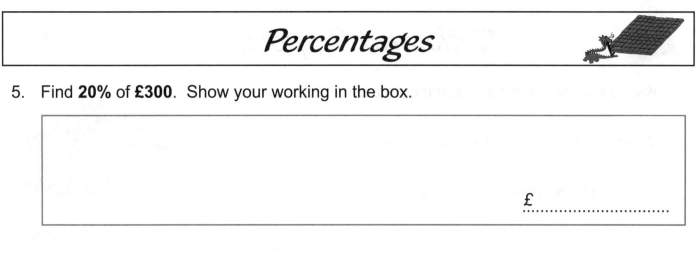

5. Find **20%** of **£300**. Show your working in the box.

£ ....

6. Sam is trying to save **£600** for his holiday. He has saved **£240** so far.

   What percentage has Sam saved? Circle the answer below.

   | 20%   50%   24%   40%   60% |

7. The large square below contains **12** identical small grey squares.

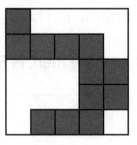

   What percentage of the square is shaded? .... %

8. Place these values in order from smallest to largest.

$$\frac{12}{100} \qquad 10\% \qquad 0.11 \qquad \frac{4}{50}$$

smallest ——————————————→ largest

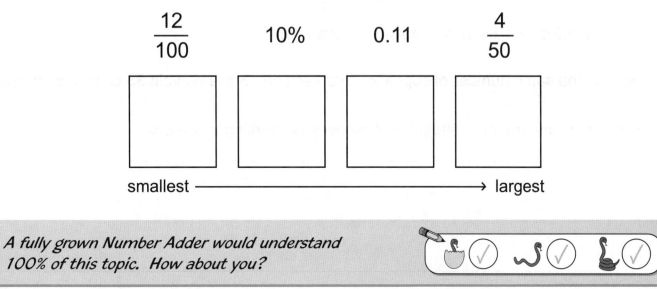

A fully grown Number Adder would understand
100% of this topic. How about you?

Ratio and Proportion

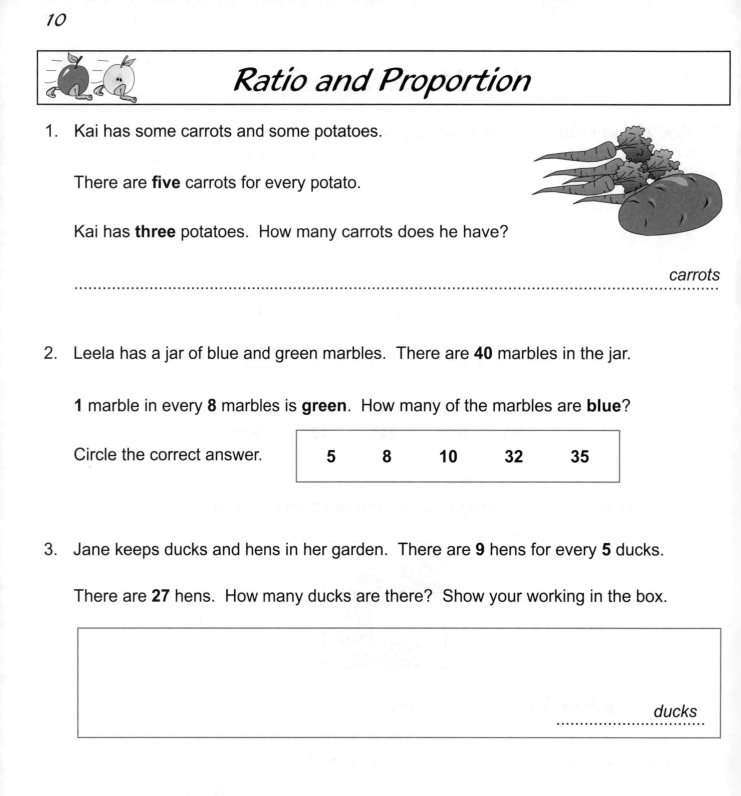

1. Kai has some carrots and some potatoes.

    There are **five** carrots for every potato.

    Kai has **three** potatoes. How many carrots does he have?

    .... *carrots*

2. Leela has a jar of blue and green marbles. There are **40** marbles in the jar.

    1 marble in every **8** marbles is **green**. How many of the marbles are **blue**?

    Circle the correct answer.

5	8	10	32	35

3. Jane keeps ducks and hens in her garden. There are **9** hens for every **5** ducks.

    There are **27** hens. How many ducks are there? Show your working in the box.

    .... *ducks*

4. Jake has **56** cupcakes to put into some cake tins.

    He puts the same number of cupcakes into each tin. **5** tins contain **35** cupcakes in total.

    How many tins are there altogether? Show your working in the box.

    .... *tins*

Ratio and Proportion

5. A grocery sells fruit boxes which include
    four oranges, three apples and one banana.

    One day they sell **48** oranges in their fruit boxes.

    How many apples did they sell?

    ....

    How many bananas did they sell?

    ....

6. Six chocolate eggs cost **£2.40**. How much do ten chocolate eggs cost?

    £ ....

7. Here is a recipe for pancakes:

Pancake Recipe
250 ml milk
120 g flour
60 g butter

    Grace makes some pancakes using **480 g** flour.

    How much butter does she need?

    .... g

    How much milk does she need?

    .... ml

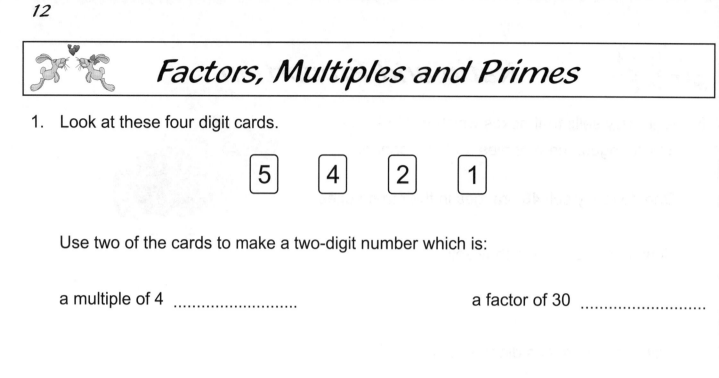

Factors, Multiples and Primes

1. Look at these four digit cards.

    $\boxed{5}$ $\boxed{4}$ $\boxed{2}$ $\boxed{1}$

    Use two of the cards to make a two-digit number which is:

    a multiple of 4 ....   a factor of 30 ....

2. Circle all the multiples of **6** in the box.

18	20	22	24	26

3. Write down all the factor pairs of **48** in the box below. One has been done already.

    1 and 48

4. Put a number less than **20** in each section of the table.

	multiple of 5	not a multiple of 5
odd	....	....
not odd	....	....

Factors, Multiples and Primes

5. Look at this number sequence.

    Fill in the next two numbers.

    3,   11,   19,   27,   35, ☐ , ☐

    Will **92** be part of the sequence? Circle: **YES**   or   **NO**.

    Explain your answer below.

    ....

    ....

    ....

6. Circle the prime numbers in the box.

2	7	9	17	27
31	39	45	49	

7. Write a prime number in each box to make these calculations correct.

    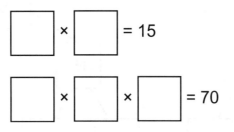

    ☐ × ☐ = 15

    ☐ × ☐ × ☐ = 70

8. Which **two** prime numbers are factors of **all** the numbers in the box?

20	30	40	50	60

    .... and ....

Factors, Multiples and Primes

9. Chris has a bag of sweets. There are more than 20 sweets in the bag.

    He shares his sweets equally between six people.

    Chris says, "The number of sweets in the packet was prime."

    Is he correct? Circle: **YES** or **NO**.

    Explain your answer below.

    ....

    ....

    ....

10. These diagrams are called **factor trees**.

    Each number is split into two factors.
    These factors are written in the boxes underneath the number.
    This is done until only prime numbers are left.

    One of the factor trees below has been done for you. Complete the other one.

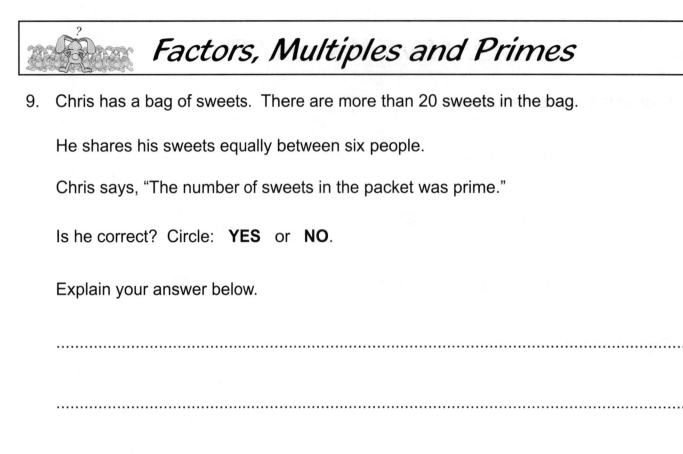

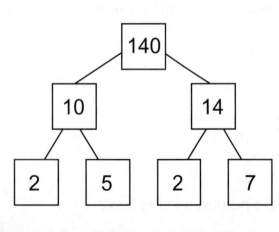

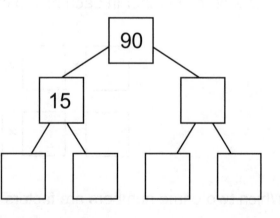

A Number Adder in its prime has no problem with this topic. Have you got the x-factor too?

Square Numbers

1. Circle the square numbers in the box below.

27	36	40	49	80	100

2. What is **eight** squared?

    ....

3. Use the answer to 5 × 5 to help you find **50 × 50**.

    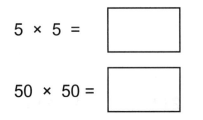

    5 × 5 =

    50 × 50 =

4. Put a number under 40 in each section of the table.

	multiple of 4	multiple of 6
square	....	....
not square	....	....

5. Fill in the boxes:

    Which two square numbers add together to make **34**?

    and

    Which two square numbers have a difference of **51**?

    and

Square Numbers

6. Work out the value of 90^2.

....

7. Work out the value of $3^2 + 4^2$ in the box below.

    Is your answer another square number? Circle: **YES** or **NO**.

8. What is **110** squared? Circle the correct answer.

121	1212	12100	12121	110110

9. Chloe thinks that **4900** is a square number.

    Is she correct? Circle: **YES** or **NO**.

    Explain your answer below.

    ....

    ....

10. Put a two-digit square number in each box to make these calculations correct.

    $\boxed{} \times \boxed{}$ = 400 $\boxed{} \div \boxed{}$ = 4

Number Adders don't go round in circles when it comes to square numbers. How about you?

Adding and Subtracting

1. Calculate the following in your head, and write the answers in the boxes.

60 + 20 [ ]   80 + 90 [ ]

170 – 40 [ ]   210 – 60 [ ]

2. Draw a line between the two numbers that have a difference of **60**.

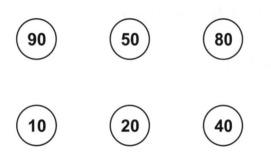

3. Circle the three numbers that add up to **2300**.

| 500 | 600 | 700 | 800 | 900 |

4. Write numbers in the boxes to make these statements correct.
   One has been done for you.

7000 is three thousand less than [*10 000*]

9000 is two thousand more than [ ]

3000 is five hundred less than [ ]

8000 is two hundred more than [ ]

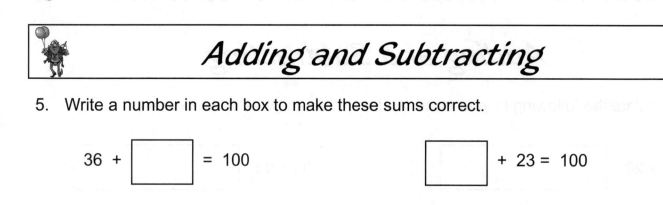

Adding and Subtracting

5. Write a number in each box to make these sums correct.

36 + ☐ = 100

☐ + 23 = 100

☐ + 68 = 100

49 + ☐ = 100

6. Emma has **125 g** of jelly sweets. Harry has **249 g**.

How many more grams of sweets does Harry have?

Use the box for your working out.

.... g of sweets

7. Fill in the missing digits to make these correct. One has been done for you.

493 + 3 | 4 | 8 = 841

271 + 3 | ☐ | 2 = 633

2 | ☐ | 7 − 113 = 184

848 − 6 | ☐ | 1 = 207

8. Subtract **four hundred and fourteen** from **seven hundred and eight**.

Use the box to show your working.

....

Adding and Subtracting

9. A pet shop sells three types of cat food.

£2.69	**£3.48**	**£1.94**

What is the difference in price between the most expensive and least expensive food?

£ ....

Oli buys a tin of the most expensive food and a tin of the least expensive food.

How much does he have to pay?

£ ....

10. Calculate 2451 + 348 + 59. Use the box for your working out.

....

11. Match the numbers which have a difference of **12**. One has been done for you.

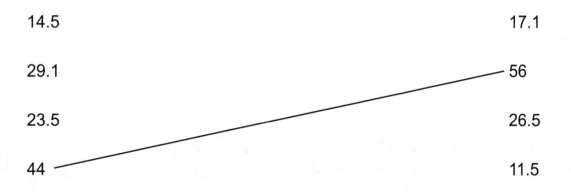

14.5   17.1

29.1   56

23.5   26.5

44   11.5

Adding and Subtracting

12. A sack of flour weighs **25.3 kg**. A baker takes out **15.8 kg**.

   How much flour is left? Use the box for your working out.

   .... *kg*

13. Fill in the missing digits to make the calculations correct. One has been done for you.

   45.3 − 21. [8] = 23.5   63.1 − 25. [ ] = 37.2

14. Circle the two numbers that add up to **1**.

   | 0.12 | 0.32 | 0.45 | 0.65 | 0.68 | 0.78 |

15. Toby has a twenty pound note to spend in the newsagents.

   He wants to buy a magazine for **£2.95** and a box of chocolates for **£8.69**.

   How much money will he have left? Show your working.

   £ ....

Adding is what Number Adders do best!
How about you? Tick the box to show how you did.

Multiplying and Dividing

1. Circle the numbers in the box that divide exactly by **five**.

| 15 | 2 | 31 | 25 | 8 | 30 | 45 | 60 |

2. Fill in the boxes to make these calculations correct. One has been done for you.

$3 \times \boxed{7} = 21$

$\boxed{} \div 6 = 5$

$8 \times 9 = \boxed{}$

$54 \div \boxed{} = 6$

3. Lyn writes down the multiplication **4 × 8 = 32**.

Use the same three numbers to write another multiplication and a division.

$\boxed{} \times \boxed{} = \boxed{}$

$\boxed{} \div \boxed{} = \boxed{}$

4. Work these out in your head:

Fifty-six divided by eight ....

Thirty multiplied by five ....

Thirty-six divided by four ....

Fifty multiplied by seven ....

Multiplying and Dividing

5. Write in the missing numbers. One has been done for you.

$2100 \div \boxed{21} = 100$ $3400 \div \boxed{} = 100$

$970 \div \boxed{} = 10$ $11\,000 \div \boxed{} = 1000$

6. Write in the missing numbers.

$3.9 \times \boxed{} = 390$ $2.7 \times \boxed{} = 27$ $0.4 \times \boxed{} = 400$

7. What is:

forty-five divided by ten?   ....

six hundred and eleven divided by one hundred?   ....

nine hundred and ninety-nine divided by one thousand?   ....

8. Ali thinks of a number. He divides it by 100. His answer is **42.8**.

What number did Ali think of? Circle the answer.

$\boxed{0.428}$ $\boxed{428}$ $\boxed{4.28}$ $\boxed{4280}$ $\boxed{42\,800}$

9. Fill in the missing numbers.

$0.052 \times \boxed{} = 52$ $\boxed{} \times 100 = 41.9$

$10 \times \boxed{} \times 2.95 = 2950$ $28\,643 \div \boxed{} = 286.43$

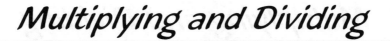

Multiplying and Dividing

10. Add brackets to the calculations below to make them correct.

$$8 \times 9 - 2 = 56$$

$$12 + 8 \div 4 = 5$$

11. Calculate **27 × 8**. Use the box for your working.

....

12. Miss Jones hands out coloured counters to a group of children in her class.

She has **51** counters. Each child gets **seven** counters, and there are **two** left over.

How many children are the counters shared between?
Use the box for your working out if you need to.

.... *children*

13. Ethan needs **70** lollies for a party. The lollies he wants come in packs of **4**.

How many packs does he need to buy? Show your working in the box.

.... *packs*

Multiplying and Dividing

14. Circle the two divisions which have an answer of **4 remainder 1**.

| 23 ÷ 6 | 33 ÷ 8 | 13 ÷ 3 | 19 ÷ 5 |

15. Work out **70 ÷ 3**. Give the remainder as a fraction. Use the box for your working.

$$70 \div 3 = \boxed{} \quad \dfrac{\boxed{}}{3}$$

16. Work out **46 × 52**. Use the box for your working.

....

17. A box of porridge oats weighs **1495 g**.

    How many grams of oats are in six boxes? Show your working.

...........................*g*

18. Write in the missing numbers in these calculations. Use the box for your working.

$$\boxed{} \div 3 = 172$$

$$6 \times \boxed{} = 792$$

Multiplying and Dividing

19. Work out these multiplications. Show your working in the boxes.

194 × 28

....

257 × 16

....

20. Work out these divisions. Show your working in the boxes.

714 ÷ 17

....

858 ÷ 26

....

21. Write a single digit in each box to make this calculation correct.

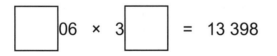

☐06 × 3☐ = 13 398

22. Underline the correct answer in each box.

3.8 × 9 =
3.42
34.2
342

61.4 × 3 =
1.842
18.42
184.2

10.7 × 4 =
4.28
42.8
428

Multiplying and Dividing

23. Fill in the missing numbers.

$$6.3 \div 9 = \boxed{}$$

$$1.7 \times 8 = \boxed{}$$

$$\boxed{} \div 6 = 0.4$$

24. A ticket to see a film at the local cinema costs **£4.95**.

A group of six friends go to see a film.

How much do they pay in total? Use the box for your working.

£ ....

25. Work out the following. Show your working in the boxes.

3.57 × 8

....

46.8 ÷ 9

....

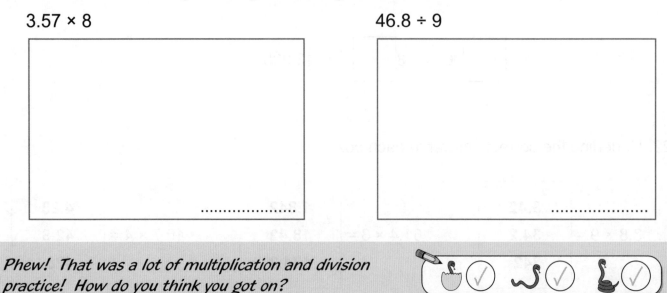

Phew! That was a lot of multiplication and division practice! How do you think you got on?

Checking Calculations

1. Dawn does the sum **34 + 12 = 46** in a maths lesson.

    What inverse calculation could she use to check her answer? Tick the box.

    ☐ 46 + 12 = 34   ☐ 34 − 12 = 46   ☐ 46 − 12 = 34

2. 36 ÷ 12 = 3.

    Circle the multiplication below that correctly uses the same numbers.

36 × 12 = 3	12 × 3 = 36	36 × 3 = 12

3. Draw a line to join each calculation to its inverse. One has been done for you.

    15 + 3 = 18   45 ÷ 3 = 15

    15 ÷ 3 = 5   18 − 3 = 15

    15 × 3 = 45   18 + 3 = 21

    21 − 3 = 18   5 × 3 = 15

4. Here are some multiplications.

    For each multiplication, write a division that uses the same numbers.

    29 × 3 = 87   ☐ ÷ ☐ = ☐

    18 × 9 = 162   ☐ ÷ ☐ = ☐

Section 2 — Written and Mental Calculations

Checking Calculations

5. Dan wants to work out the answer to **51 − 19**.

    Write a simpler calculation in the box below that he could use to estimate the answer.

    [   ]

    Dan thinks that 51 − 19 = 42. Explain why Dan cannot be correct.

    ....

    ....

6. Uzma pays for herself and three friends to get into a football match.

    The total cost is **£64**.

    She thinks the tickets cost £16 each.

    Write a multiplication she could use to check her answer.

    [   ] × [   ] = [   ]

    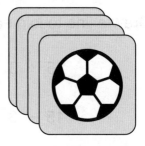

7. The answer to a sum is **290** when rounded to the nearest 10.

    What is the smallest number the actual answer could be? Circle the answer.

    | 281 | 284 | 285 | 289 | 294 |

    What is the biggest whole number the actual answer could be?

    Write the answer in the box: [   ]

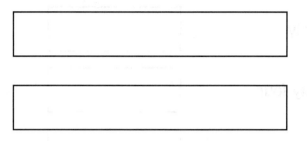

Checking Calculations

8. Write two calculations you could do to check **112 ÷ 14 = 8**.

9. Estimate 9.1 minus 3.8 by rounding to the nearest whole number.

    Fill in the boxes with your estimated calculation.

10. Circle the best estimate of the value of 17.9 × 10.2.

    170   190   210

        180   200

11. Ben buys 9 cakes at a bakery. The total cost is **£28.35**.

    Use rounding to estimate the cost of each cake.

    Ben says, "£28.35 ÷ 9 = £3.15, so each cake cost £3.15."

    What calculation could he use to check his answer? Write one in the box.

Mental Maths

1. Work out the following in your head:

   half of seventy

   double twenty-four

   a third of sixty

   three times thirteen

2. What number is:

   sixty-five less than eighty-seven? ....

   twenty-nine more than thirty-eight? ....

3. Josh has **65** pence in his left pocket. He has **73** pence in his right pocket.

   How much money does he have in total?

   £ ....

4. Jenny is **seventeen** years old.

   Her brother Owen is **thirteen** years older than Jenny.

   How old is Owen? .... *years old*

   Their grandmother is **sixty-two** years older than Jenny.

   How much older is she than Owen? .... *years older*

Mental Maths

5. Naz wants to buy **eight** pencils.

   Pencils cost fifty pence each.

   How much change will he get from a ten pound note?

   £ ....

6. Look at the shopping list.

   Yams cost **one pound** each.

   A pepper is half the price of a yam.

   A tomato is half the price of a pepper.

   Find the total cost of the shopping on the list.

   Shopping

   2 yams

   3 peppers

   4 tomatoes

   Total:

   £ ....

7. Lily picks a number card from a pack.

   She doubles the number on the card and then adds thirty.

   Her answer is **54**.

   What is the number on the card?

   ?

   ....

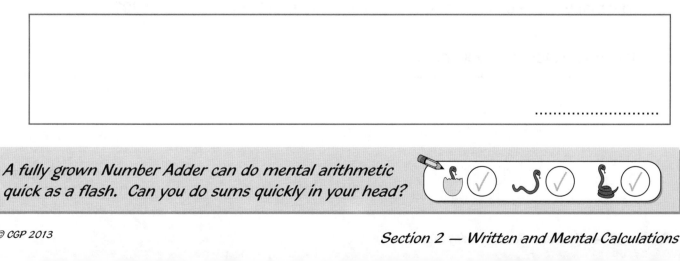

A fully grown Number Adder can do mental arithmetic
quick as a flash. Can you do sums quickly in your head?

Wordy Problems

1. Jon and his brother want to catch a morning train from Seatown to Snowlet.

    The timetable is shown:

Morning Train Times	
Seatown	09:25
Skyville	09:50
Snowlet	10:35
Sandford	10:50

    How long is the journey between Seatown and Snowlet? Tick the box.

    ☐ 25 minutes   ☐ 1 hour 10 mins   ☐ 1 hour 25 mins

    The full price of a train ticket is **£9**, but students can travel for half the price.
    Jon is a student but his brother is not.

    How much will they have to pay in total for their train tickets?

    £ ....

2. Rachel washes cars to raise money for a charity.

    She gets **£5** for each car she washes.

    How much will she get for washing **9** cars?

    £ ....

    How many **more** cars will she have to wash to meet her target of **£100**?

    Use the box for your working out.

more cars ....

Wordy Problems

3. Max has **12** toy cars.

   Fred has exactly two and a half times as many cars as Max.

   How many toy cars does Fred have? Circle the answer.

6	18	24	30	36

   Max and Gina have **fifty** toy cars in total.

   How many toy cars does Gina have?

   .... *cars*

4. Theo is choosing sweets in a sweet shop.

Jelly Frogs	**Chocolate Mice**
27p for 100 g	48p for 100 g

   How much will it cost for 300 g of Jelly Frogs?

   .... *p*

   How many grams of Chocolate Mice can Theo get for **12p**?

   .... *g*

5. There are **180** sheep and cows in total on a farm.

   There are 30 more sheep than cows. How many of each are there?

   [   ] sheep   [   ] cows

Number Adders need to be good at words as well as numbers. Are you a whizz with these wordy problems?

Number Patterns

1. Put a cross through all the squares on this number grid that contain a number that is both a multiple of **3** and a multiple of **5**. One has been done for you.

1	2	3	4	5	6	7	8	9	10
11	12	13	14	~~15~~	16	17	18	19	20
21	22	23	24	25	26	27	28	29	30
31	32	33	34	35	36	37	38	39	40
41	42	43	44	45	46	47	48	49	50
51	52	53	54	55	56	57	58	59	60

2. Here is a repeating pattern of numbered shapes.

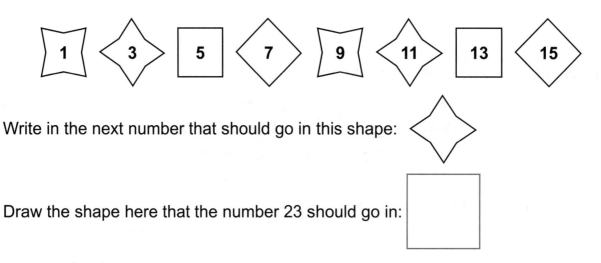

Write in the next number that should go in this shape:

Draw the shape here that the number 23 should go in:

3. Here is a Venn diagram for sorting numbers.

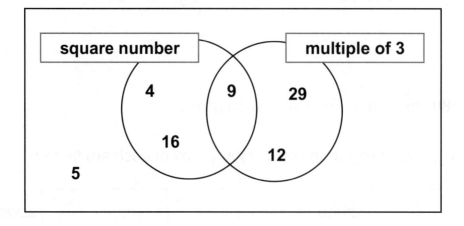

Which number is in the wrong place? Cross it out on the diagram.

Write the number **36** in the right place on the Venn diagram.

Number Patterns

4. This sequence follows the rule:

> **"to get the next number, multiply the last number by 3, then subtract 10"**

Fill in the next 2 numbers in the sequence.

6   8   14   ☐   ☐

5. Write the missing number in the sequence below.

240   120   60   30   ☐

What is the rule for the sequence? Underline the answer.

> **subtract 120 from the last number**
>
> **double the last number**
>
> **halve the last number**

6. Here is a sequence of three shapes shaded on a grid.

Shade in the next shape in the sequence.

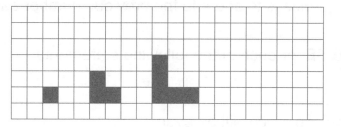

How many squares will be shaded in the seventh shape in the sequence?

Explain how you know this.

....

....

Number Patterns

7. Kate writes a number sequence with the following rule:

> **"to get the next number, subtract one from
> the last number, then double the answer"**

The sequence contains the number 130.

Find the number **before 130** in the sequence. Use the box for your working.

....

Kate thinks that the number 515 will be in the sequence. Explain why she is wrong.

....

....

8. Here is a sequence of numbers. It continues in the same way.

| 6 | 10 | 14 | 18 | 22 | ... |

The rule for this sequence is to add 4 to the previous number each time.

Circle **TRUE** or **FALSE** for each of the following statements.

Every number in the sequence will be even.   **TRUE / FALSE**

Every number in the sequence will be a multiple of 4.   **TRUE / FALSE**

There will be a prime number in this sequence.   **TRUE / FALSE**

There will never be a multiple of 7 in the sequence.   **TRUE / FALSE**

Number Patterns

9. This sequence of numbers follows the rule:

> **"square the position of the number in the sequence and add one"**

Fill in the missing numbers in positions 2 and 5 in the sequence.

2 [ ] **10   17** [ ] **37**

10. Raj is making a shape sequence using matchsticks.

Shape			
Shape number (**n**)	1	2	3
Number of matchsticks (**m**)	5	9	13

n stands for the shape number, which is the shape's position in the sequence.

m stands for the number of matchsticks used to make the shape.

Raj uses the formula below to find the number of matchsticks needed for a shape:

$$m = (4 \times n) + 1$$

How many matchsticks are needed to make shape **9**?

....

What is the shape number of the shape that uses **21 matches**?

....

Number Patterns

11. A game show has five boxes, each containing money.

    Two of the boxes are labelled A, two are labelled B and one is labelled C.

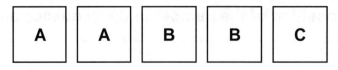

    Boxes with the same letter contain the same amount of money.

    The five boxes contain **£100** in total.

    The game show host opens a box labelled A and finds **£10** inside.

    Write in the boxes below a possible pair of values for the amounts in boxes B and C.

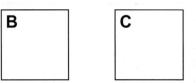

12. Look at the sequence of bead designs below.

    Design number (n):   1   2   3   4

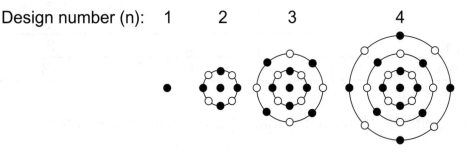

    Complete the table to show how many beads are used in each design.

Design number (n)	1	2	3	4	5	6
Number of beads (b)	1	9	17			

    Complete the rule that links the number of beads (b) with the design number (n).

$$b = (\boxed{} \times n) - \boxed{}$$